StoneS

Writing and art by ki

Editor's Note

In this issue, things go missing. There is a woman who has lost her husband and is now losing her mind. There is a girl whose best friend goes missing. There is a boy who is rushed to the ER after hitting his head at the playground and momentarily forgets where he is and why. There's a bowl of light that loses its light when brought to Earth, and an ode to the beauty of the simple eraser.

This theme seemed appropriate as we begin to enter spring—a time when we begin to wake from what feels like hibernation. How quickly every year I forget the cold, dark days of winter! And so much else along with them—how to dress in warmer weather, what to eat. Somehow, every year, I figure it out. What seems to be missing is still there, embedded in my body, which often seems to know more than my mind.

This March, consider writing a story about someone, or something, emerging from a real or metaphorical winter. What do they choose to remember? What do they forget?

Editor in Chief
Emma Wood

Director
William Rubel

Operations
Sophia Opitz

Typesetter
Jeff Piekarz

Production Coordinator
Carmela Furio

Blog Editor
Caleb Berg

Customer Service
Tayleigh Greene

Refugee Project
Laura Moran

Stone Soup (ISSN 0094 579X) is published eleven times per year—monthly, with a combined July/August summer issue. Copyright © 2023 by the Children's Art Foundation–Stone Soup Inc., a 501(c)(3) nonprofit organization located in Santa Cruz, California. All rights reserved.

Thirty-five percent of our subscription price is tax-deductible. Make a donation at Stonesoup.com/donate, and support us by choosing Children's Art Foundation as your Amazon Smile charity.

To request the braille edition of *Stone Soup* from the National Library of Congress, call +1 800-424-8567. To request access to the audio edition via the National Federation of the Blind's NFB-NEWSLINE®, call +1 866-504-7300, or visit Nfbnewsline.org.

Cover:
A Quirky Combination
(Colored pencil and pen)
Sabrina Lu, 13
Virginia

StoneSoup
Contents

ART

Evening (iPhone SE)
Nora Giuffrida, 13
Washington, D.C.

The Bowl in the Sky

A magician helps a poor peasant bring the moon to Earth

By Kamalama Mick, 13
Hawai'i

Once there was a poor peasant who lived on the outskirts of the village. Every day, from dawn to dusk, he labored in the fields—plowing, sowing, and reaping crops. His only payment was a cup of rice, which he took home for his dinner and ate in his common rice bowl.

Usually, after he ate, the peasant went straight to sleep so that he would be ready for the next long day of work. But one night, he decided to go outside for a few minutes to look at the stars.

As he sat on the steps, gazing up at the glimmering pinpricks of light, something caught his eye. He turned and beheld the quarter moon above him. The glowing half-circle seemed to call to his soul.

The peasant had only ever seen the moon on full-moon festivals, when it was at its roundest, and as he gazed open-mouthed at the shining shape, he thought, *It is very like my rice bowl.* In fact, so bowl-like was its shape that he decided it *must* be a bowl.

"And surely," he said to himself, "such a shining bowl must be filled with the riches of the sky."

Riches! In a bowl in the sky! "I must bring it down to Earth!" he exclaimed. "And then I shall never need to work in the fields again, for I will possess the silver of the heavens."

So he reached up a hand to pull the bowl from the sky. But no matter how hard he pulled, all he grasped was empty air.

Well, he thought, undiscouraged, *surely it will take magic to pull a bowl from the sky.*

Then he remembered the magician who lived far away at the edge of the mountain.

"I'll go find him," the peasant declared. "He will know how one might pull a bowl from the sky." So he left his house and walked across the plain towards the mountain.

The journey took him seven days and nights. He crossed fields and rivers, found his way through thick forests, and climbed steep hills. Sometimes the road he followed was wide, and sometimes it was nothing but a thin, trampled trail through the brush. Yet at last he stood at the door of the magician's hut.

He knocked on the door, and almost immediately it was opened by the magician. He was very tall and wore a cloak of stars, and though the peasant looked right at him, never afterward could he recall the magician's face.

"Yes?" crackled the magician, his eyes sparkling with wisdom and seeming to see into the peasant's soul.

"Seven nights ago, there was a bowl in the sky!" cried the peasant. "I am sure that it is filled with riches. How do I pull it to Earth?"

The magician was silent for a while. Then he reached into his pocket and pulled out three thick vines. "Braid these into a rope and create a lasso," he advised. "Then use it to capture your moon bowl."

The peasant stared at the vines wonderingly and thought, *Each vine is only a foot long. How can they possibly reach into the sky and pull down the bowl?* But he did not question the magician.

He walked a short distance away and sat down under a gnarled tree, through whose branches the full moon shone. He began to braid . . . and braid . . . and braid. It did not take him a few minutes as he had expected. Instead, he braided for a hundred days and a hundred nights while the moon bowl came and went, came and went. Yet his braiding never seemed to reach an end.

Until one night, finally—it did.

Then the peasant noticed that spread all around him was a long rope, ready to capture the bowl. He knotted it into a lasso and went out under the sky, the cool night air swirling around him. And there was the bowl, sinking slowly towards the distant hills in the west. The peasant gazed at it and smiled, thinking about all the riches it must hold, and with that he threw his lasso . . . and missed.

Six times he threw the lasso, and six times it thudded to the earth—empty. But each time, it was a little farther away. And then he pictured his home and how it would look filled with the silver of the sky, and he threw the lasso once more.

He looked up to see it sailing through the air, higher and higher until he couldn't see its end, so far stretched the rope. Suddenly he felt it grip something, and it tugged so strongly it almost yanked him off his feet. But he braced himself and pulled as hard as he could. Strong from working in the fields, he pulled and pulled with all his might until at last he saw the bowl begin to move towards him.

Closer and closer it came until finally it lay before him—his bowl, much larger than it had looked in the sky. Eagerly he ran forward to look inside.

But to his dismay, the bowl was gone! There was only a large round rock—and not even a bit of it was glowing.

The peasant was shocked. "I saw my bowl; it was caught in the lasso!" he exclaimed. "Where did it go?"

He heard a rustle behind him and turned to see the magician approaching, his eyes the same color as the purple twilight sky above.

"Where has it gone?" the peasant asked, crestfallen.

"The moon bowl does not belong on Earth," murmured the magician. "If it comes here, the bowl's light vanishes, and it turns dark. Its true place is in the heavens."

The peasant looked up at the darkened sky. It looked empty without the brilliant bowl lighting it up. "But what about the riches?" he asked. "I was so sure they were there!"

"They belong in the sky as well, for only there are they real," the magician explained. "But fortunately, you do not need them."

"Why not?"

"Because you are rich already. In your hard work, in your determination, in your acceptance. And in your closeness to the Earth, to nature, and to the moon and stars in the dark night sky." The magician looked at him. "In such ways are we all rich from birth."

The peasant looked back. And suddenly he understood.

It was the bowl itself that made him rich. At night, it shone with the silver of the heavens. It would always be there, while money would not.

He slipped the lasso off the dark rock and knelt beside it, placing his hands beneath its smooth, round surface. It was as light as his precious common rice bowl, and he had no trouble lifting it off the ground.

Then he pushed it lightly upwards, and it rose off his hands and floated away.

He and the magician watched it as it flew higher and higher—glowing brighter and brighter as it went. Then at last it stopped, hanging in the western sky, shining as though all the stars were filling it with light.

The peasant gazed up at it peacefully. He knew now where the true riches lay.

Gold and silver were only echoes of the real thing.

And that meant that he, the peasant, was richer than he had ever believed.

Rising

By Oola Breen-Ryan, 11
Connecticut

I go
for a walk today.
The world is alive—
birds swooping and singing like phoenixes,
red, yellow, orange dahlias,
their petals bursting
as if they think that they are fireballs.
We see
a dead bumblebee on the sidewalk.
I bury it,
my cold hands on its delicate body.
Maybe it
too
will rise from the ashes.

Bright Morning (Gouache)
Hannah Francis, 12
California

Two Poems

By Holly Jane Doyle, 10
Ireland

Waxwings

—these men, heading down to
the berry bar after a shower
and a touch of hair gel on
top of their fluffy, feathery heads.
Going down with a dollar, hoping
to get a fresh juicy berry the
size of a bunny's tail.

Wood Oysterlings

Quiet in the wood.
Robins hop from branch to branch.
Gently, the branch sways—
        up down—again—up down
and stops.

The breeze weaving around the trees
pushes plants over.
Leaves jostle together.
My footsteps odding out of the sounds.

Above, raucous rooks haw and caw
while landing on branches.
Ever so suddenly they take off—
each a flapping ink blot across
winter's gray sky—
coughing out their caws.

Below, little ears listen.
Growing and spreading with all the sounds
they hear. They listen in every moment, to
every creature, every step I take, every crow
that haws, constantly.

Fossils (iPhone 6)
Anna Weinberg, 12
Washington, D.C.

A Lonely Sailboat (iPhone 6s)
Adam Ganetsky, 13
Massachusetts

Lost and Forgotten

A slow morning takes an ominous turn for a widow

By Alexandra Steyn, 13
Connecticut

The moment her foot touched the pavement, she stopped. She turned around, uncertain about what she was doing, the action having completely vanished from her mind. Nothing jumped out at her or returned the memory. She sighed. It had happened yet again.

Shaking her head, she walked, defeated, back to her house, which squatted on the top of the street, firm and resolute despite its size. The early morning sky of pale yolk hung behind it, creating an imposing silhouette. The last owner told her it had stood there for a century, and she reckoned it would stand there for many more centuries to come.

The door swung open with its usual welcome creak, ushering her into the kitchen. She half expected Mell to be there, sitting in his usual spot as he sipped coffee and calmly read the paper, which lay open on his crisply creased pants. It was one of his many constants, a sort of reassuring activity he always completed even if a hurricane raged outside.

Of course, nothing of the sort happened. It had been months, and there were many more stretching out before her before she joined him. She had stopped the daily newspaper delivery a few weeks ago when her pain had become unbearable, but now a new pain ached every time she glanced at the empty place the newspaper had once held on the kitchen table.

Wondering whether she should start up the newspaper delivery again, she heated up the frying pan and gloomily cracked the eggs into the pan, moving through the movements she knew by heart. They sizzled for a moment then settled down, and she turned back to the table, frowning as if there were something she had been thinking about moments before. Unsurprisingly, she couldn't remember for the life of her. Shrugging, she returned to her eggs, certain that what she had been thinking wasn't important.

Once they were done, she shook the eggs out of the pan and onto her plate, setting it down in her usual spot and slumping into the chair. As she ate, her eyes traveled over the cracked ceiling, the cabinets whose paint was fading, the rotting floorboards dotted with holes, and the windows long ago sealed over by thick layers of dust. Eventually, she knew she would either have to sell the house and move on or spend thousands of dollars helplessly trying to save it from plunging even deeper into the thick moat of disrepair. It broke her heart. She could still remember the shrill, laughing voices scampering between rooms, the feisty anger of a denied child, and the blustering tears over a scraped knee; later, the quiet hours spent poring over one page of a textbook, the anxious look as they awaited their exam results, and the pure excitement and joy reminiscent of childhood flitting gleefully across their faces before vanishing within moments as they quickly regained the teenage mask of gloom and doom.

The halls had been empty for a long time now, the rooms shells of their former selves and hidden behind doors that had been closed for so long she'd forgotten if they were locked or not. Another thing lost, another thing forgotten. It was becoming the mantra of her life.

Her eyes turned back to her plate. Subconsciously, her hand traveled around its rim, rubbing the well-worn porcelain with her fingers, finding the nooks and crannies of long-ago cracks created by years of disregard, carelessness, and neglect that had turned into an ocean of tiny fractures. The plate wasn't how it was meant to be—it was supposed to be perfect, uncracked, in mint condition despite its old age—yet somehow, it gave her a sense of belonging. She was supposed to be in good health too; she was still in her sixties, a good few decades away from death, despite her husband's passing. But her memory was failing her, and it was no fault of her age but rather of a specific kind of disease that had the misfortune of choosing *her* to fall upon. The name . . . it was on the tip of her tongue. She knew it. She knew it. She knew it, she knew it, she knew it. But it wasn't there. It felt just out of reach, like a dream you know you remember when you wake up and swear that you do, and yet you can't recall any details.

She dumped the remains of her eggs into the trash and was walking towards the dishwasher when she stopped, staring at the plate in front of her and squinting at the cracks, unsure if she had ever been thinking about them. Shrugging, she slipped it into the dishwasher, the thought already fleeing out the window.

Once again, she slid into her seat, this time with a mug of coffee in her right hand, the pale white of the milk mixing into the richer colors of chocolate brown and velvet black. Inhaling, she sat back with the coffee-cinnamon aroma melting around her. She'd taken to adding a dash of cinnamon to her coffee each morning. It was something Mell had done she had always scorned him for, and now it was too late to admit to him how amazing it was.

A few cars creaked and groaned by, but other than that, the road was peaceful, another lazy day with many more to come. Of course, she still had so much to do. But, to no surprise, she was putting that off. Yet to what end? It was a question she couldn't, or perhaps wouldn't, answer.

A dog and his owner jogged by, the dog wagging his tail happily in the sunlight, the man's labored breathing causing her to flinch and look away from the window, studying her mug instead. The milk had faded into the jaws of the dark colors, and she leaned forward to take a sip—

A startled cry burst out from down the street. Muted noises echoed around

Glass Half Full or Half Empty (Acrylic)
Shaivi Moparthi, 12
Texas

the block. Wincing, she set down her cup and heaved herself up. She'd never been able to resist helping someone in need, and she wasn't about to give up today, give up on the one thing that told her *Your life isn't for nothing.* But what if it really was all for nothing? Her good intentions hadn't been able to save Mell. And if they couldn't save him, who she had loved more than anything, how could they save anyone else?

She shrugged off her worries and shrugged on her favorite coat, the black one with silver buttons, ivory lapels, and deep pockets in which she had lost hundreds of little odds and ends, things like bottle caps and wrappers and loose change, all things that Mell had passed for trash but she had kept as little mementos, never entirely sure what gave her the urge to slip them into one of the coat's pockets.

She buttoned her coat one by one, her withering fingers fumbling around; the amount of time it took her to button her coat seemed to grow longer each day. She stepped into her boots, thick, ugly, gray ones her daughters would frown at had they been there. But they weren't, and that was fact, just like Mell wasn't there.

Stepping out of the door, she was met by the sudden brightness of the sun shining down on her and the biting cold, which wrapped around her neck and sank its fangs into her flesh. She couldn't remember the last time she'd been outside. She tramped down her driveway and turned the corner, shading her eyes from the sunlight as she tried to find the source of sound. Whatever it was, it was disguised, but the sounds still barreled towards her, piercing and shrill. As she drew nearer, she could make out a man's high-pitched voice screaming. Then—nothing. Silence. Quiet. The screams stopped just as soon as they had started. That chilled her more than anything.

Ahead, there was a slight bend in the road full of trees and bushes which blocked her view of what lay beyond. She took a deep breath and mentally prepared herself, blocking out all thoughts of what it could be and hoping that it would just be someone who was overreacting.

She headed around the corner and stopped abruptly, eyes widening as she took in the scene before her. Her heart dropped to her gray boots, then rose to her gray hair, then back down again, up and down as if it were on a roller coaster. As fast as she could go, she whirled around, but no one was behind her. At least the assassin wasn't after her. Silently, she cursed her do-gooder self that had wanted to come here in the first place. She came expecting to find a child with a scraped knee, or a barking dog its owner couldn't control. Instead, she fell upon this. Well. It was her fault.

She nudged it with one foot. It didn't respond. She poked it. It didn't respond. She lifted it. It didn't respond. It confirmed her suspicions.

Stepping around the liquid and ignoring the way the crimson reminded her of Mell's favorite couch back at the house, she reached for her phone, which she had slipped into one of her pockets before she left. (Thank goodness she remembered which pocket it was in; otherwise she would have spent hours searching uselessly for it.) Without thinking, her hands dialed the number, and she pressed the phone to her ear, quaking with fear but starting to smile from relief with the knowledge that he would know exactly what to do. The steady rings ran out, patient and even, and despite their volume, they were somewhat calming. Then:

"You have reached Mell Pondle. Please leave a message."

She took the phone away from her ear and stared at it, eyes roving around the screen. He was probably busy, at a work meeting or grabbing lunch with a colleague or in a heated debate with one of his clients. She could talk to him later, and he knew to call her back. Heaving a sigh, she put her phone away and turned back to the matter at hand.

Something clicked in her. A memory returned. A fortune, a gift. If only it were something happy. But no. It was a crushing blow, like every other time she'd forgotten that Mell wasn't there and wouldn't be there.

She took out her phone and threw it across the road.

She took out all her mementos and stomped on them.

She screamed manically for twenty minutes.

She did none of these things.

She refused to lose her calm disposition and cool head on top of everything else. A part of her screamed that she already had. She'd lost it the moment her children had packed up and left, and she'd lost it again the moment Mell went. No. She silenced that with a quick, effective slap to the head. At least, she thought it was effective. It waited five seconds, then came back, more persistent this time but with a different saying.

There's nothing you can do, it told her.

She ignored that and inspected the body before her.

There's nothing you can do, it repeated.

Silence, she snapped back. *I'm trying to focus.*

There's nothing you can do! it shouted.

She looked down. The voice was right; it was beyond help. She turned on her heel, kicking up dust, and started to walk away, turning her collar up and thrusting her hands deep into her pockets where they mingled with her odd mementos. A question occurred to her. Was she hiding from and protecting herself against the cold, or something else? Or perhaps both? She pushed away these thoughts as useless, a product of too many hours spent aimlessly without anything to do, and hiked up her driveway, thoughts drifting towards the book she wanted to finish that day.

She stepped into the warmth of her house, kicked off her gray boots now speckled with red, and unbuttoned her coat and hung it up, giving it a fond pat and a forlorn smile. Wandering into the kitchen, she spotted her half-finished mug and sauntered towards it. She took it up in both hands and dropped into the same seat, frowning. The coffee had long since turned cold, the colors losing their richness and turning dull and muddy, looking more like dirt than an appetizing drink. She set it back down again with a clink and pushed it away.

Turning her attention to the window, she stared outside, mesmerized by the streaming sunlight glinting off the pavement. When was the last time she'd been outside? She couldn't remember.

Discovering the Magic of Erasers

A meditation on erasers

By Xi Huang, 10
New York

Erasers are pure magic. Think—a simple little block that lies snugly in your palm. With a motion from your hand, it neatly removes all the ugly strokes and smudges from the paper, no matter what paper it is and what texture it has, noiselessly. A perfect bar of soap, except with a distinct rubbery smell, it can scrub off all the unwanted lines—fat or thin, dark or light, streaks of graphite and sometimes even blotches of ink!

This tool is surprisingly durable and convenient too. There is no sharpening or polishing needed to use it. To erase, all you need to do is rub it on a surface, and the eraser will do the rest, as it gobbles up all the graphite. Erasers last for an astounding amount of time, helping you correct mistakes and eliminate marks. Rubber ones feel especially durable because they are hard and can be squeezed and bent without breaking.

The eraser presents astonishing variety as well. Soft, hard, ink erasers, rubber, pencil-top erasers, gum erasers, vinyl, squishy, moldable kneaded erasers (like a chunk of magical dough)…and though they serve the same purpose, all have their own special qualities. Kneaded erasers, for example, do not leave the rubbery dust that reminds one of the remaining crumbs of an eaten cake. Rubber ones are smooth and as velvety as a mouse. Gum erasers are extraordinarily soft and dusty, and may look rather chewy, but instead of being like gum, they tend to crumble when used. Erasers come in a huge assortment of shapes and sizes and colors—think of all the different ones in the world! And yet, it is such a simple thing, so useful and easy to grasp.

Imagine a world without erasers—a world smeared and gray and stamped and smudged, a world piled to the brim with incorrect grammar and spelling, a world overflowing with rewritten answers and essays, a world of frustration—and you will come to see the startling importance of this plain, basic, humble object that fits in your fist.

Deep Blue (Acrylic)
Saira Merchant, 12
Texas

Catch of the Day (Acrylic)
Ivory Vanover, 12
Texas

Two Poems

By Shivanshi Dutt, 13
New Jersey

My Different Names

When I was small,
Around preschool,
I was called
Anusha.

For some reason,
One that I still do not understand,
My mother and father decided
To change my name.

In a legal process which took *ages*,
And tons and tons of pages,
My name transformed
Into something new.
Suddenly,
I was *Shivanshi.*

I said it to myself,
Trying it out on my tongue.
Shi-van-shi, Shi-van-shi.
It sounded good.
Strong and firm.

It takes a while for people to get it.
They say,
Shrivanshi
Or
Savanshi.

Some people call me Shiv,
Just because they are too lazy
To take the time to say it right.

I am called other things as well.
Things that I like.
By my friends and family,
I am called Shivi.
To me it sounds fun and playful.
Every time it is said, it reminds me of
Our closeness.

By my best friend of all,
I am called Ivi.
A short name,
So short that it couldn't possibly represent all of our friendship,
But it does.

Monochrome (Mixed media)
Emily Yu, 14
Hong Kong

art room

i want to sit in the art room
where no one thinks to check on me
i want to sit in the art room where no one dares to enter
without knowing what they are going to say
and say quietly
i want to sit in the art room so there is no room
for anyone else
i want to sit in the art room
so there is room
for myself

Girl (Acrylic)
Nari Woo Park, 10
Massachusetts

With Expression Comes Connection

The narrator celebrates the beauty of ballet

By Kayla Song, 13
Connecticut

Since I was three years old, ballet has played a huge role in creating and shaping my life. Looking back about ten years, I can see it has made me a more emotionally aware person. I don't have much to say about starting ballet. It was mostly a parental decision around the time I was getting pretty skilled at walking. But it was a good move on their part. I'm a normal person, not too shy, not too loud. I'm just right. And I think that's because of the power of ballet, whether I understood it or not when I started. All I knew was it was fun and I felt happy, excited, and like I was celebrating something when I did it.

That's what ballet is really all about—celebration and emotionally significant events. Ballet began in the early fifteenth century as a way to convey the emotions of things like weddings and celebrations. To dance is to express deep or strong emotions, and ballet is the best of all dance forms (in my opinion) for doing that.

Although ballet has become more formal since it began, its purpose—to help people express their emotional, celebratory, and spiritual feelings—remains the same. I certainly celebrate when I dance, but ballet has also taught me the importance of other emotional expressions. It's also helped me get in touch with myself when I'm feeling something I don't have the words for. If I'm sad but happy, or frustrated and angry, or feeling overwhelmed or excited, I can dance. I don't have to find someone else to listen to me. I don't have to have a friend or partner or teammate to go to. I can dance alone. I can do ballet in a gym, a field, on the sidewalk, in my room, or the kitchen as well as on a stage. Ballet requires no special equipment, balls, goals, or nets. Ballet only requires a heart and emotions of any sort that need to be expressed.

Some emotions can't be expressed with words, and ballet enables me to tell a story without words. It allows me to express small feelings or large ones, complex or simple feelings. Ballet is for communicating something for which no words exist in any language. Driven by my emotions, ballet physically captures the complex thoughts that live in my head and provides a way for them to escape, to communicate so others can see and feel them too.

Although a person's facial expressions hint at a speaker's true thoughts or feelings, ballet involves the entire body! I've learned that my body—from my hands to my legs and head—gives away what I am feeling through the way that I move. When I dance, I am exposed, vulnerable, open to anyone who watches; even if they know nothing about ballet, they know about emotions, and ballet touches them and they know better what I am feeling. I love that.

When I am happy, my movements are sharp and bright, and when I am sad, my movements are slower and low-spirited. When I am anxious or upset, my performance suffers because my movements lack emotion. An audience sees that, and we are bound, if only for the length of the performance, by our shared feelings. We remain strangers, yet we become very intimate at the same time. Unlike many stage performances—acting, music, or comedy—only ballet reaches out and involves the audience in the performer's emotional state. It's very personal.

Yes, music can strongly impact an audience, but the listeners are responding to the instrument and the sound, not the person playing it so much—unless it's a solo performance. Music as a part of ballet is more powerful. It has a huge role to play in a ballet performance by directly influencing the tone and thereby our (the dancer's) emotions and the audience's feelings as well. In performances like *The Nutcracker*, for instance, I have learned the importance of connecting with the audience by embodying the emotions present in the music. When the music is more upbeat, I am inclined to make happier movements. When it is "legato," or smoothly connected, my movements follow suit, smoothing and connecting in tandem with this quality.

This allows me to really get into my character and capture the attention of the audience. They respond to the music, but even more to my movements. The combination of music and movement doubles the power of the story.

Because the emotions are genuinely felt as a result of the musical influence, my performance feels more authentic, and an audience can sense this and embrace it as well if they choose to. We connect deeply on an emotional level. We are not trapped in the mental world of words but in the world of fears, hopes, dreams, emotions, and deep yearning or celebration. We "flow" through the story on an emotional level.

Like words, physical movement is a way of communicating our experience. Ballet, with its strong emotional and visual power, allows the audience to not only understand its characters better but to empathize with them, and to better visualize things—as though they were seeing the sunset and feeling the air cool as the rays of the sun grew fainter. As my ballet teacher always says, "With expression comes connection." Her mantra reminds me of the importance of real expression as a means of connecting with my audience.

Through ballet, I have learned a lot about what it means to really perform, to give all of one's true self and feelings. Ballet, at its purest, is performers expressing their genuine emotions and wholeheartedly becoming their respective characters. Ballet is authentic. Over the years, I've learned that ballet is much more than just mastering delicate technical movements and choreographies. An expert performance means my every movement conveys true emotion, so that my audience can interpret and experience the story too. That attention to authenticity as a ballet dancer has made me a more authentic person as well, more aware of my own emotions and feelings, as well as how I express them. I don't think I can separate emotion from movement anymore. They are connected— from the simple movements we make cooking, hugging, walking, or getting out of bed to the complex moves we make when we're happy or sad, celebrating or grieving. Life, at its best and purest form, is dance, and the most expressive form of dance is, in my opinion, ballet.

Grass Jewels (iPhone XR)
Ella Shin, 9
New Jersey

My Raindrop Journey

A little raindrop goes on a big journey

By Roy Zha, 7
California

Hello. My name is Roy. I live in a big, big cloud. One day, I felt a bump on my shoulder and other raindrops squeezed me tight. I had to leave this cloud. But how?

A few days later in the morning, I realized I was falling in midair! A bird came by and he tried to swallow me! The bird missed because I was falling rapidly!

Suddenly I felt something under my foot, and I landed somewhere mysterious. I felt so sad. No one was with me. Then, I suddenly realized it was night! Well, perhaps I had to sleep. "Sleep tight," I said to myself.

The next day, when I woke, I realized I was floating. This can't be real! *It's just a nightmare!* I thought.

Then I started to rise. I rose faster, then faster and faster, and I couldn't control myself from rising! Quickly, I rose back to the sky! After that, a small cloud stood in front of me. He asked me if I wanted to join. "Yes!" I said.

Just like that, the journey began again—again and again. Each time I felt something new; each time, it was very scary. Believe me or not!

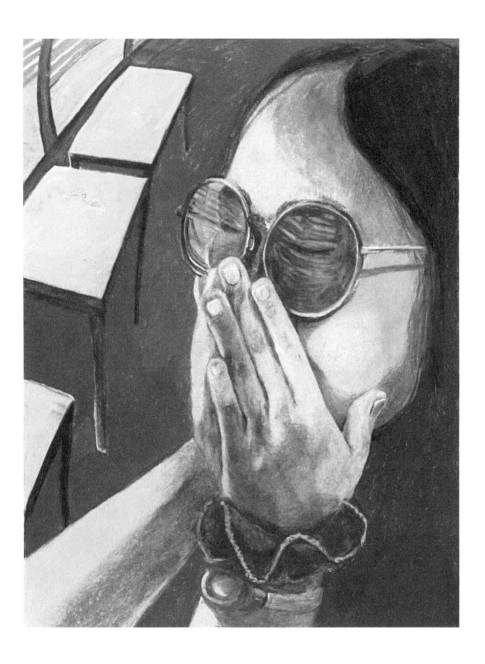

Yellow Light (Colored pencil)
Eileen Moon, 12
Washington

The Kidnapping of the Principal's Son

When her best friend disappears, Katie puts on her detective hat

By Cecilia Hodgman, 13
Georgia

A typical Sunday night in the Midwestern town of Mells Bells included fourteen-year-old Katie up way past her bedtime typing out her latest article. Her articles covered topics ranging from the harms of pesticides to the new mayor's dog's death. Katie attended Townsend High, the local prep school, with her best friend since first grade—Xavier. Katie was there on scholarship. Xavier was there because his mom was the principal.

Tonight, though, Katie's article was a little too close to home. She furiously typed out the title: "The Kidnapping of the Principal's Son" and began hammering away.

The night before, Katie and Xavier had been hanging out after watching their favorite superhero movie at the theater in the center of town.

"Katie, you should totally date the villain in the movie. You two are so alike!" Xavier teased.

Katie punched him in the shoulder and rolled her eyes. Xavier's phone dinged, and he sighed dramatically.

"The most protective mother in the world is wondering where her awesome son is right now and insists that he return home in an instant!"

Xavier and Katie made plans to meet up the next morning, hopped on their bikes, and rode off.

When Katie woke up in the morning, she sent Xavier a text. After Xavier hadn't responded to the next three she sent, she tried calling him. When she still couldn't reach him, she called his mother, only to hear that Xavier had gone missing.

"When was the last time you saw him?" Katie asked over the phone.

"Last night, when I was saying goodnight to him," his mother replied. "I'm sorry, Katie. I really have to go. Maybe we can talk more tomorrow at school?"

"Sure, Principal Smith. I'll be there."

After finishing the call, Katie jumped into reporter-detective mode. She grabbed a couple of recent pictures of Xavier and started knocking on doors in

Xavier's neighborhood to see if anyone had seen anything suspicious last night. Katie had ridden two blocks past the movie theater—a full eight blocks from Xavier's home—before finding a single clue. Mr. Peanut, the elderly man who ran the drugstore, admitted that he had thought it was odd lights were on in the abandoned warehouse across the street. Her first clue! Katie sent a text to Xavier's mom and sped back home, keeping her eyes open for more clues about Xavier.

The next day, Katie left for school early so she could catch Xavier's mom before school started. Katie dashed to the principal's office and knocked on the door.

"Come in," said Principal Smith. Katie opened the door and walked in. Even though Xavier's mom was good at hiding her emotions, Katie noticed her hair, which was usually pulled into an immaculate bun, was in a messy ponytail today. Principal Smith also had black circles under her eyes.

"Um, hello, Principal Smith. I want to ask you some questions about when you last saw Xavier."

"Go ahead, Katie."

"Okay," Katie said, flipping through notes in her journal. "Maybe it's nothing, but you know Mr. Peanut downtown? He said last night was the first night he'd seen lights on in that old, abandoned warehouse. You think it could be connected?"

Principal Smith looked at Katie with a tired expression. "Katie, maybe we should talk about this a little more privately."

"What do you mean by 'more privately'?"

"Follow me," she said.

First, Principal Smith closed the door and the shutters, then went over to her light switch and pressed a button hidden under it. Katie's eyes widened when she saw the floorboards slowly shift to reveal a hidden trapdoor.

"Wow," Katie said, sucking in breath. "You have a secret office inside your office."

"Yes, but Katie, this is really important and you *cannot* write about it in your story, do you understand?"

"Yes, ma'am," Katie said. On a normal day, she would have been very grumpy about missing this scoop, but this was not a normal day. She followed Principal Smith down the stairway with her jaw dropped.

"Katie, before I met my husband and had Xavier, I was working for the Secret Service."

"You were a spy?"

"Something like that. I believe that may be why my son was kidnapped."

"Alright. Tell me all you know."

Principal Smith told her about all the people who could have wanted to kidnap Xavier—because of what she knew as a former secret agent and because of who she had put behind bars.

"Thank you, Principal Smith. This is very helpful," Katie said, taking notes furiously. Running up the stairs and climbing through the trapdoor, she watched as Principal Smith closed the door and set everything back to normal.

While running to her first class, she bumped into her chemistry teacher, whose golden blonde hair fell around her shoulders. Her sparkling emerald eyes caught Katie's. She had been at the school even before Principal Smith.

"Hello, Katie. Working on your newest story?" asked Mrs. Jimena Cent. Mrs. Jimena Cent preferred the students call her by her first and last name.

"Yes, ma'am. I'm working on the story of Xavier's kidnapping."

"*Kidnapping*," she said, with concern sparkling in her big, innocent eyes. "I hadn't heard. Is there any way that I can help poor Xavier? He was one of my favorite students and an excellent chemist. Have you found any clues?" Mrs. Jimena Cent asked with interest.

"I think so. I'm a pretty good reporter." Katie showed Mrs. Jimena Cent her notes so far.

"Wow, Katie. I must admit that is impressive."

Katie looked at her phone and realized that Principal Smith had called her. "I'm so sorry, but I really have to go."

Mrs. Jimena Cent nodded. "Keep looking out for clues, Katie. Best of luck."

"Thank you, Mrs. Jimena Cent." Katie walked to Principal Smith's office.

"Hey, Principal Smith. Sorry I missed your call. I was talking with Mrs. Jimena Cent to see if she had any ideas about Xavier's kidnapping."

"Yes . . . about that," Principal Smith said with a wince. "Katie, maybe you shouldn't talk about Xavier's kidnapping with other people, especially Mrs. Jimena Cent."

"I'm sorry. I don't understand," Katie said.

Principal Smith took out a folder from her desk. It had a red stamp that said "Classified."

"I found this in Mrs. Jimena Cent's desk." Katie opened the folder and saw a picture of a much younger Mrs. Jimena Cent. She was smiling up at the camera and under her picture it said *Gilm Tuly*.

"Gilm Tuly was a thief. When I was working as an agent, I caught her stealing military intelligence. Since it was all a hacking job, I tracked her, handed the info over, and never saw her face. And she never saw mine. Because we were never able to track her to her source, she only served twenty years. In my 'retirement' from the Secret Service, the agency set me up with a stable job. This was it, they said. I have since realized that they also wanted me here in case they needed more information on Tuly. She has obviously discovered my identity."

"Wait . . . I'm confused. Why does Mrs. Jimena Cent have Gilm Tuly's name?"

"Because Mrs. Jimena Cent is Gilm Tuly. Two names for the same person."

Slowly Katie saw it coming together.

"What do we do?" Katie asked with a gulp.

Principal Smith looked at her with grim eyes. "Well, considering this is top-secret stuff, I'm ordered to handle it personally. Let's meet at the warehouse tonight. Prepare for battle."

"Um," Katie said, "maybe not battle . . . how about a super-duper spy mission?"

"Sure," Principal Smith said, with a small smile. It was the first one Katie had seen since Xavier had disappeared.

At the warehouse, Katie and Principal Smith crept inside as quietly as they could. Their goal was simple—find Xavier and avoid Gilm Tuly.

Old cardboard, wood, and metal boxes littered the ground. The warehouse smelled musty. Small, flickering lights that hadn't been replaced in a long time hung from overhead. There was a door at the end of the warehouse with a small control panel on its right.

Katie and Principal Smith took a small step forward, looking through the gloom of the warehouse. They were about to go deeper until . . . *CRASH!*

In a hoarse whisper, Katie asked, "What was that?"

They ducked behind an old metal box.

Katie asked, "Is it Xavier?"

They heard Gilm Tuly walk across the room murmuring to herself.

"Does that answer your question?" Principal Smith asked sharply.

"Yep," Katie said.

For ten minutes, Katie and Principal Smith whispered a plan. It wasn't perfect, but it would have to do.

Then they put the plan in action: Principal Smith searched the room they were in for Xavier. Katie snuck behind boxes and up to the control panel, not sure if Gilm Tuly had left or was still there. She turned around, scanning the room. She looked back and saw the door close behind Gilm Tuly. She had left the warehouse.

Principal Smith came up to her and whispered, "Xavier is not in this room. Let's check the next." Katie pushed the button and they ran through the doors. They found themselves in a small room with only a computer in the center. Katie dashed up and scanned the computer. It had a question instead of a number code, and a microphone below. On the screen flashed "What does my name mean?"

"Katie, we have to answer the question, fast! We have only thirty seconds before the warehouse blows up!"

"How do you know?" Katie asked.

Principal Smith pointed at a countdown on the wall: 28.

"That's very clear." Katie groaned. Katie and Principal Smith both stared, panicking, at the question. "What does my name mean?!"

"Hurry, hurry," said Principal Smith.

10, 9, 8, 7 . . .

"Thinking . . . thinking . . .!"

5, 4, 3 . . .

"GOT IT!"

2 . . .

"I AM INNOCENT," Katie screamed into the microphone.

"Disabled," said a voice over a speaker. And the door opened.

Principal Smith gave Katie a side look. "What?!"

Katie shrugged, "Jimena Cent. Innocent. They sound alike."

They went into the room to find Xavier snoring on the ground. No guards, no traps, just him—asleep.

"Is he okay?" Katie asked

Principal Smith checked his forehead and snorted. "Sleeping drug—that's the silliest thing I've ever heard of."

"Wait, so we go through all of that trouble only to find out he was *sleeping*?!" Katie cried.

"Shhhhhh," Principal Smith scolded. "You'll wake him up."

"Serves him right," Katie grumbled.

Principal Smith carried Xavier in her arms, not slowing until they got back to her house. Katie panted trying to keep up. They put Xavier in his room, and Katie stayed with him while Principle Smith went into the kitchen.

While she was gone, Katie examined Xavier, looking for any injuries. Katie frowned, seeing a corner of notebook paper sticking out of Xavier's pocket. She carefully pulled it out, unfolded it, and read:

```
Dear Xavier,

This is your friend, Katie. I have something very important to
tell you. Meet me at the warehouse, a little ways away from the
movie theater. Come quickly—it's urgent.

Love, Katie

P.S. Do NOT in any way tell your mom where you are. I don't want
anyone to know.
```

Katie took a deep breath and looked up. This was how Gilm Tuly had tricked Xavier into coming to the warehouse that night! One of the greatest drawbacks of texting—Xavier had probably never seen Katie's handwriting.

Principal Smith walked back into Xavier's room: "I think this will do the trick."

"Why do you have an antidote for a sleeping drug in your kitchen cabinet?" Katie asked, raising an eyebrow.

"Old spy supplies. When you're a secret agent, you've got to be prepared."

"I found something," Katie said, handing the note to Principal Smith.

"This explains a lot," was all Principle Smith said when she was done reading.

"That's all!" Katie cried. "Just *this explains a lot!* Why on *Earth* would Xavier believe that—he has a lot of fluff behind his ears, but I certainly didn't think he was that dumb."

Principal Smith ignored her.

"It's also worrying that Gilm Tuly knew you and Xavier were such good friends. She really paid attention to the details," Principal Smith said.

"Why would Gilm Tuly want to hurt Xavier?"

Principal Smith sighed. "Revenge is a powerful thing. It eats some people up. And the best way to hurt someone is to hurt someone that person loves." Principal Smith leaned down and touched Xavier's forehead, her face softening.

When she spoke again, there was nothing soft in her command: "Hand me my phone. Now, we'll call the police and they'll handle Gilm Tuly."

Gilm Tuly was arrested for kidnapping the next day. Her handwriting matched that of the note found in Xavier's pocket. Xavier woke up with no memory of the kidnapping.

When Xavier read Katie's article, he laughed so hard he couldn't breathe, thinking she had switched to writing fiction. Because, of course, he didn't believe one bit that he had been kidnapped.

Katie went on to become a famous reporter and detective who specialized in solving kidnapping cases. Xavier became a dream and memory loss expert. Though Katie wrote a lot of great stories, the one that meant the most to was her article "The Kidnapping of the Principal's Son."

Brother (Canon EOS Rebel T7)
Joey Vasaturo, 12
Connecticut

Bloody Head

Samuelle comes face to face after someone who is new at the playground

By Samuelle Torres, 11
New York

I don't know why this happened. I was a nice, calm person.

I was new to the area, and I had moved there not that long ago. I was nine years old and I loved going to the park, so I asked my aunt if I could go to the park across the street from East Side Middle School. The sun was shining bright like a spotlight, and the clouds looked like they were filled with happiness and joy. The birds were tweeting, and it was a good day to be outside, but I instantly got kind of bored because there were usually a lot more kids. All of the kids there were little. Then I saw a group of kids who were around my age or older, so I asked if I could possibly play and they all agreed. We were five to six kids playing hide-and-seek.

After playing for a while, I saw someone who went to my school, P.S. 198 Elementary School, and was in third grade. He was picked to be the seeker. I was afraid because I was a shy kid back then, so I ran with Casey and hid under a jungle gym bridge. The seeker was near, so I decided to get up and run, but I got up too fast and cracked my head on the jungle gym bridge. Casey screamed like she had just seen a ghost. Her mother came and saw me and yelled to her husband. "Honey, come help!" she called out. Her husband came running in a dash. My head was bleeding.

All these questions came rushing through my bloody head:

What happened?

What had I done wrong?

They brought me to a bench nearby, and I noticed the sky wasn't blue anymore. It was gray. The birds weren't tweeting anymore. I wasn't smiling anymore, and everything looked like an upside-down happy face. Casey's dad picked me up from the bench, put me in the backseat of their car, and drove us all the way to the nearest hospital called Mount Sinai.

When we got to Mount Sinai, Casey's parents got me out of the car. I felt a weird tingle from my head, but not from the bleeding. It was something else. Then, something switched off in my head and I didn't know where I was anymore, like a kid in a cornfield. When I looked around, I noticed that I was in a place that I didn't like. I started having thoughts like:

Where am I?

Who are these people?

Are they going to hurt me?

I panicked slightly and started to wiggle out of Casey's dad's grip. He started to tighten it. I said to myself, *The only way out is to use all of my strength.* So I bit his hand and ran toward the exit, but just then a doctor walked in. I bumped right into her.

I looked up sharply as she bent down slowly and stared me deep in the eyes. She noticed what was wrong with me and said, "I understand you are lost. Okay? Please, follow me." So I got up and started to follow her down the hall on the left side of the exit.

I kept wondering where she was taking me, until we walked into the emergency room. When we walked in, it felt so familiar to me. I looked at the doctor's name tag. It read "Uira." Then it hit me. This was the same room where I was born, and that was one of the doctors who had helped my mom give birth to me.

At that moment, another doctor came in with some type of liquid and told me to drink it. I was confused and I thought there was no way I was drinking that. "Please?" said Dr. Uira.

"What is it?" I asked.

"It's for your head," she said.

Then the other doctor said, "Drink it and follow me." I gulped it down as I jogged to catch up with her. We went to room G15.

I looked around the room and saw a small sink, an examination table, and doctor tools. I sat on the table and looked around. The doctor left and came back in with a purple drink and a metal tool. "Drink this," she said.

"Okay," I replied and drank it.

Dr. Uira brought me to another room where my aunt also was. Dr. Uira bent down to look at me and said, "I need you to be strong for this one. Try to stay still. This will hurt because we're putting in stitches."

At the time I didn't know what stitches were, but I was still nervous because they sounded painful. Still, I trusted her. She opened a packet with a disinfectant wipe and began to clean the wound on my head. I felt a pressure on the wound and a light sting. Then she gathered the suture supplies and prepared to operate on my head. Before she began the procedure she said, "I'm going to count to three. At the end of three, you will feel three sharp pains, but try your best not to move." She counted to three and began to stitch my head. I wanted to yell, but I felt like I couldn't. As painful as it was, the doctor finished quickly. Before I knew it, she was done.

Dr. Uira stood up. "Okay, now follow me again," she said. That time, I was unsure if I should, but I did, and I was greeted by Casey and her parents. My aunt, my friend Casey, and her parents, all asked if I was okay.

"I guess." I shrugged. My aunt hugged me.

"Let's go home," she said.

Earnest Eyes (Acrylic and watercolor)
Saira Merchant, 12
Texas

The Mask

By Lily Guttermuth, 12
Montana

I sit and stare
At the mask I have to wear.
When I go to school,
I see a sign that says,
"Wear your mask and be cool."
I feel like a caged bird.
I get no say,
Not in any way.
I feel too self-conscious at recess to take it off.
Or when I cough.
After a year and a half of being stuck in this place,
I start to feel
ashamed of my face.

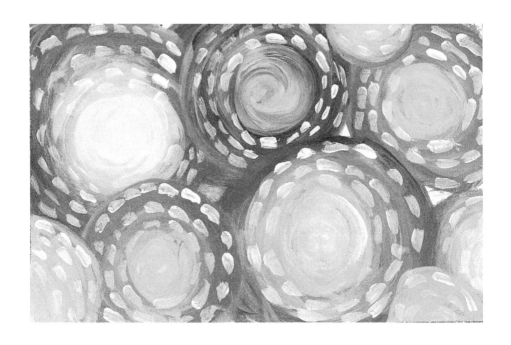

Dream Dream (Oil)
Sophia Zhang, 12
Texas

Reading with My Sister

The narrator talks about mornings reading with their sister

By Minghan Tang, 12
New York

When I was four years old, I moved to America with my mom and older sister and brother. I remember the first year being very strange and different from our life back in China. We didn't have a car, so we had to walk everywhere we went, and coming from a walkable town, we were unaccustomed to everything being so far apart in the suburbs.

All around, there were people we'd never met, and it was hard for us to communicate with anyone outside of our family because we barely knew how to speak English. My older brother was already in high school and very busy, so this made it even more important to spend time with my sister.

When school started that first year for her, my sister began to read me picture books in the mornings. We'd sit together on the slightly crooked front steps of our new house as she waited for the school bus, and she would trace her finger over the illustrations as she read to me. I remember that the mornings smelled like freshly cut grass, and the leaves swayed in the trees above us. I loved being with my sister, and reading with her helped me feel less empty when I didn't have anyone to play with after she left for school.

Once I got to kindergarten, we had less time to read together, and as time went on, we had completely forgotten about it. I would really like to read again with my sister. Now, years later, she is about to go to college next year, and I feel sad thinking about not reading again with her. Thinking about those mornings together brings up a lot of bittersweet feelings!

Sometimes I wish I could reverse time just so I can experience reading with her on those sunny days again, and I feel sad that I will see her so much less next year. I can't stop that from happening, but you readers who have siblings might still have time to spend wonderful days together, reading and laughing.

So, what are you still doing reading this? Go outside and read with your family!

Highlight from Stonesoup.com

From the Stone Soup Blog

The following is a transcript of part of the second installment of Emma's poetry podcast. Head over to our blog at Stonesoup.com/young-bloggers/ to listen to it or read it in full!

Poetry Soup (A Poetry Podcast)
— Episode #2

By Emma Catherine Hoff, 10
New York

Hello, and welcome to *Poetry Soup*! I'm your host, Emma Catherine Hoff. Each episode, I'll discuss a different poem and poet. Today, I'll be talking about two different poets—one real and one fake.

Can a poem be written by someone who doesn't even exist? "The Keeper of Sheep" is written by Alberto Caeiro, which is a heteronym invented by the poet and writer Fernando Pessoa. A heteronym is different from a pseudonym because a pseudonym is just a name, while a heteronym is an entire personality. I'll talk more about the heteronym Alberto Caeiro later. But first, a little bit about Fernando Pessoa.

Fernando Pessoa was born on June 13, 1888, in Lisbon, Portugal. When Pessoa was six years old, he made up his first heteronym, a man by the name of Chevalier de Pas. Pessoa created at least seventy-two heteronyms throughout his lifetime. Pessoa was a poet, writer, literary critic, translator, publisher, and philosopher. He was deeply influenced by English poets like William Shakespeare and Percy Bysshe Shelley. You can also see the influence of Walt Whitman in much of Pessoa's work, including the poem we'll be reading today. Fernando Pessoa died on Nov. 30, 1935, in Lisbon, Portugal, at the age of 47.

But now there's another poet to talk about: Alberto Caeiro. In creating Caeiro, Pessoa had to come up with a whole new personality with an entire history. Caeiro has had only a grade-school education—he is a peasant who is in touch with his surroundings and is greatly influenced by them, yet not curious about their existence. According to Pessoa, Alberto Caeiro does not question the things around him—he has interesting ideas, but he simply takes in his surroundings without asking "why." Speaking in the voice of another heteronym, Ricardo Reis, Pessoa said, "Caeiro, like Whitman, leaves me perplexed. We are thrown off our critical attitude by so extraordinary a phenomenon. We have never seen anything like it. Even after Whitman, Caeiro is strange and terrible, appallingly new." The perspective of the poems changes based on the personality of the heteronym Fernando Pessoa might be writing under at the time. Octavio Paz even called Caeiro the "innocent poet."

Head to our website to read or listen to the rest!

About the Stone Soup Blog

We publish original work—writing, art, book reviews, multimedia projects, and more—by young people on the Stone Soup Blog. You can read more posts by young bloggers, and find out more about submitting a blog post, here: https://stonesoup.com/stone-soup-blog/.

Honor Roll

Welcome to the Stone Soup Honor Roll. Every month, we receive submissions from hundreds of kids from around the world. Unfortunately, we don't have space to publish all the great work we receive. We want to commend some of these talented writers and artists and encourage them to keep creating.

STORIES

Luisa Lamb, 11
Ayush Parmar, 11
Yueling Qian, 11
Kyla Tavares, 12

POETRY

Valerie Huang, 7
Maya Jimenez, 6
Miriam Kubo, 10
Mason Li, 9
Avery Shaughnessy, 11

ART

Lilian Jean Newton, 11

CPSIA information can be obtained
at www.ICGtesting.com
Printed in the USA
BVHW021949130223
658422BV00006B/101

9 780894 091469